STORIES FOR Bedtime

Brown Watson
ENGLAND

Princess Poppy

Princess Poppy lives in a grand castle at the top of a steep hill. She is a very lucky little girl because she seems to have everything she could ever wish for. She has rooms full of toys and wardrobes filled with beautiful clothes and shoes. She has her very own hairdresser who accompanies her every minute of the day in case a hair strays out of place. She has dozens of personal servants and there is even someone to read her books to her!

Princess Poppy should be the happiest little girl in the world, but she is probably the most bored little girl in the world! Looking out of her bedroom window, high up in the tower, she sees the cook's three children helping with everyone's chores down in the yard. They look to be having so much fun. She decides to join them, so she picks out her prettiest dress and daintiest shoes and skips down the stairs to meet them. The children are helping the groom to clean the stables and they are covered in straw and dust.

When Poppy asks if she can join in they take one look at her pink dress, sparkly shoes and manicured nails and burst out laughing. Poppy turns to go before they see her tears. As she crosses the courtyard the groom feels sorry for her and hands her a pile of old clothes that he's grown out of. He tells her to come back when she's got changed. Poppy is back five minutes later and this time the children are happy to let her join in.

Poppy is grubby and tired after cleaning the stables and feeding the horses but she can't remember the last time she enjoyed herself so much. Now Poppy spends a lot of her time helping the groom, the gardener and the cook or just playing with her new friends. The children also like spending time in Poppy's room, with all her toys and books and they enjoy dressing up in Poppy's fabulous clothes. Poppy thinks it's much more fun to share and she loves being with her new friends.

Timmy the Tug Boat

Timmy is a little tugboat with big ideas. He wants to be a lifeboat and rescue people in danger. But the big lifeboats laugh at Timmy and tell him he is far too small to be of any help. They look so important and busy that Timmy tries to keep out of their way. He spends most days just chugging up and down the coast, keeping a look out for anyone in distress.

One day, as Timmy is passing the cliffs near the beach, he hears frantic barking. It seems to be coming from one of the caves. Timmy knows that the caves are fun to explore at low tide, but as high tide approaches, the caves begin to fill with water. Timmy thinks the dog must have gone inside the cave at low tide and now it is trapped. Timmy rings his bell to alert the lifeboats and nervously waits outside.

Two big strong lifeboats arrive within minutes.

'Stand back, Timmy. You can leave this to us,' they call. The boats take turns to try and squeeze through the narrow cave opening, but they are far too wide. The dog sounds really frightened now and Timmy worries the rising sea might soon sweep it away.

Timmy decides he must help and launches himself through the opening. He reaches the stranded dog, seconds before a big wave sweeps into the cave, covering the very rock the dog had been clinging to. When Timmy emerges from the cave with the grateful dog, it's to a hero's welcome from the big lifeboats. From now on, brave little Timmy will patrol alongside the big boats, because who knows when they may need him next!

The Tooth Fairy

Have you ever heard of the Tooth Fairy? She is a tiny little creature, only about the size of your thumb. When children's teeth fall out, the Tooth Fairy collects them.

The next time you lose a tooth, put it under your pillow when you go to bed and leave a little note with it. If you are lucky, the Tooth Fairy will take the tooth and leave a coin in its place.

The Tooth Fairy has to work very hard because there are hundreds of teeth to collect every night. She takes them back to a magic land where all the fairy folk live.

They use the teeth to build beautiful castles and palaces for the Fairy King and Queen. But the Tooth Fairy doesn't like bad teeth, she only picks clean, white baby teeth, which fall out by themselves. So don't forget to clean your teeth every day until they sparkle.

Rainy Day Puppets

It's raining today and Roseanna and Francesca are trying to think of something to do. Mummy asks them to look under their beds to see what they can find. Between them, they discover three odd socks and an old black glove. The girls put their finds on the kitchen table, where Mummy has laid out felt tips, buttons, glue, scissors and some scraps of material.

Mummy helps the girls to sew on button eyes and draw noses and mouths on the socks. Then, using the glue, they stick multicoloured strips on them to make hair. The hand puppets look really cool and Roseanna and Francesca can't wait to show them to all of their friends.

'But what shall we make with this old glove?' asks Roseanna.

Mummy draws two cross-looking eyes and sticks them on the glove. The children still do not know what it is supposed to be.

'Put the glove on, Francesca,' says Mummy. Now the girls see what it is: a five-legged spider! 'Cool!' they laugh.

Monster Feast

The giant troll in Monster Castle is having a cookery competition and the castle is heaving with hundreds of fairies and witches, all hoping to win the huge chest of gold, which is first prize.

Fairies and witches don't really get on, so from the towering, black castle, you can hear voices screeching and squabbling, and pots and pans clanging and banging, and clouds of steam, smoke and stars pouring out of the kitchen windows!

One by one most of the cooks are eliminated, until only two finalists remain. These are Fairy Nuf and Witch Wayupp. They bring their final three dishes to the long table in the Great Hall.

Fairy Nuf has made moonshine soup, followed by flutterby wing salad, and for pudding she has made sunlight syllabub, served in a bluebell cup. Delicious! Witch Wayupp has cooked bats' ears in filo pastry, followed by a main course of fried toads in a red wine sauce, and finally there is a magnificent tower of frog spawn profiteroles! Not so delicious!

Suddenly, just as everyone is wondering which meal the troll will choose, he grabs Fairy Nuf and Witch Wayupp and crams them both into his mouth! The witch jams her broom between his jaws and Fairy Nuf quickly casts a spell, which shrinks the troll to the size of a spider. He scuttles away into a nearby mouse hole. The terrified witch and fairy realise that teamwork has saved them from a horrible fate and from that day on, all the witches and fairies remain good friends

The Greedy Pirate

Captain Rich Pickens is a very greedy pirate. He captures ships and sails away with all their gold and jewels. But his pirate ship isn't very big, and gradually, the hold, the deck and each of the rooms has filled up with treasure. The pirate crew are worried that their ship may sink, and ask the captain if they can go home, but greedy Captain Pickens doesn't know when to stop! Then, one breezy April afternoon, the lookout spies a galleon on the horizon. The pirates race after the ship and capture it.

The ship is full of precious jewels and coins but the captured captain warns the pirates that their ship will not be able to withstand the extra weight. The crew agree with their prisoner, but Captain Pickens will not listen and orders his men to haul a giant treasure chest on board. The ship begins to groan under its heavy burden. Then, quietly at first, there is the sound of splintering wood and nails popping. The crew realise the ship is breaking up and throw the chest into the sea. But it is too late so they rapidly abandon ship.

All except Captain Pickens, who refuses to leave. He is soon ankle deep in water! The captain of the other ship is back in charge and he offers to help the men if they give up piracy and come and work for him. The crew are happy to agree as they have had more than enough piracy now. Captain Pickens refuses to join them, so he is sent off in a little rowing boat.

He'll probably spend the rest of his days rowing around the site of his sunken ship, trying to work out ways of salvaging his treasure! Some people never learn!

Donny Digger

Little Donny Digger lives on a building site where a new supermarket is being built. Each day, Donny watches the big diggers preparing the ground. They scrape out great piles of earth and lumber back and forth across the building site, looking very important. Donny longs to join in but the big diggers tell him he's far too small and he'll just get in the way. Poor Donny!

Each of the Diggers has a big strong driver, but one day a new driver arrives who is much shorter than the others. It's difficult to find the right machine for Tommy, as most diggers are too big for him. When Tommy sees little Donny, he realises they suit each other perfectly. Donny and Tommy are very good at doing all the fiddly little jobs that are hard for bigger diggers, and that makes them a very happy pair.

Mike's Mermaid

Mike lives by the seaside, in a pretty bungalow at the end of the beach. From his bedroom window he watches the waves splashing onto the sand and filling up the rock pools.

In summer the beach is covered with holiday makers, but in March the sands are empty and it becomes Mike's special place. Mike's mum watches him from the kitchen window as he explores the beach.

Mike likes to scramble over to the rock pools to see what the tide has washed in. Today he dangles his toes in the cold water and fishes for crabs and shrimps with his net. Under a big clump of seaweed he can see two beady eyes and the tip of a claw. A fat pink crab is hiding under there. Mike is trying to catch the crab when a head suddenly pops over the rocks. It's a little blonde girl, with shells and seaweed in her long wet hair.

The girl is called Marina and she seems to know an awful lot about the creatures in the pool. Mike and Marina spend hours collecting sea creatures in Mike's bucket, until his mummy calls him home for tea. Mike would like Marina to come for tea with him, but Marina giggles and says it would be impossible. She says it's time for her to go home too.

Mike wants to play with Marina again so she tells him to send her a message.

When Mike asks Marina for her address, she says he should write a note, put it in a bottle and throw it in the sea! Mike thinks that would be great fun, but surely the normal post would be better? Then he sees why she wants the message in a bottle. As she waves goodbye and dives back into the sea, he sees that Marina has a shiny green tail, covered in scales. 'She's a mermaid!' thinks Mike. 'I can't wait to tell my friends!'

Do you think they will believe him?

Danny's Dinosaurs

Danny is dinosaur mad! He has a huge collection of plastic dinosaurs and he knows all their names, even the really long ones! Danny's teacher has asked all the children in his class to bring something in that interests them, so Danny brings in his dinosaur collection.

The teacher is very impressed with Danny's dinosaurs and asks him to tell his classmates a bit about them.

Danny tells everyone that the word dinosaur means 'thunder lizard'. These gigantic lizards lived 140 million years ago, before there were people on Earth! They came in all shapes and sizes, and they have wonderful names. He picks up the first dinosaur. 'This is a BRACHIOSAURUS, the biggest dinosaur ever. It was much,much taller than a house!'

TYRANNOSAURUS REX, was a very fierce dinosaur, which had teeth as long as a man's hand!

The PTERODACTYL was a flying dinosaur, with wings like a bat. Danny explains to the other children that the the 'p' in pterodactyl is silent. Next is TRICERATOPS, with its frilly neck made from bone, and its three horns. This is Danny's favourite. The COMPSOGNATHUS was the smallest dinosaur. It was about the size of a chicken. The last dinosaur is a PACHYCEPHALOSAURUS Even Danny has trouble pronouncing that name! They are also called bone-heads because they use their heads as battering rams.

When Danny has finished, the teacher hands out paper and crayons and the children draw dinosaurs all morning. The teacher then unrolls a long piece of wallpaper and sticks the drawings all over it. Then the children colour in the background with trees and volcanoes and finally, they have a huge landscape, full of dinosaurs.

It looks fantastic and the children are so pleased. They all think dinosaurs are very interesting and they hope Danny will be able to bring his collection to school again soon!

Wendy's Wood

Wendy looks out of her bedroom window towards the wood at the bottom of the garden. All the leaves in the wood have fallen on the ground during winter, so it's difficult for Wendy to recognise all the different trees. Her big brother, William, says there are lots of clues in the wood and offers to help. Wendy runs off to find her wellies. William tells her to look for an oak tree first.

Wendy knows acorns come from oak trees, so she looks high up above her for some squirrels, which eat acorns. She quickly spots a couple and follows them to a sturdy tree with a dark, rough trunk. Under the tree she finds lots of old, dried leaves. 'Found one!' she laughs. She pops a leaf in her pocket. Next she looks for old conkers, which are the fruit of the horse chestnut tree. She often plays conkers with her friends so she should easily recognise this tree.

William says horse chestnut leaves have five to seven fingers. She soon spots one and pockets it, then she rushes off to find a sycamore. They have squarish leaves with three to seven fat fingers. William says sycamores have smooth tree bark and seeds like helicopers! When Wendy finds a seed, she drops it and watches as it spins slowly down to the ground. The silver birch is easy to spot because of its white bark. The holly tree is easy too with its Christmassy leaf.

horse chestnut

oak

silver birch

sycamore

holly

Soon, Wendy's pockets are bulging with dried leaves. When she gets home she traces round the leaves and labels each picture. Then she sticks them in a scrapbook, ready to take to school on Monday. William thinks Wendy's teacher would like to see the scrapbook. The teacher thinks the book is wonderful and gives Wendy a gold star! Later, all the children in Wendy's class are taken on a nature ramble and they have fun making their own leaf scrapbooks. Why don't you try it?

The Golden Tree

Stories of Wilfrid Wizard, Winifrid Witch and their golden tree have stopped many brave men from venturing into the Wild Wood. None who have entered the wood in search of the tree have ever returned, and so the legend lives on. Anthony lives in a village just outside the Wild Wood. He plans to find his way to the wizard and witch's cottage and bring back a branch of the golden tree.

The branch should bring him fame and fortune, and then he will be able to ask the beautiful Miranda to marry him. One sunny day, Anthony rides off into the wood. He is gone for many weeks and Miranda worries that she will never see him again. When Anthony finally emerges from the wood he is very tired and miserable, but everyone wants to hear his story. Anthony tells them that he searched the woods for weeks and weeks before he came across a derelict old cottage.

The building had not been used for centuries. He knew that the witch and wizard had once lived there because inside he found old spell books along with mysterious looking jars and a broken cauldron. In the garden Anthony uncovered a cracked headstone where Wilfrid and Winifrid had been buried hundreds of years ago. Next to the headstone stood a tree covered in golden blossom, but there was nothing special about this tree. It was just an ordinary yellow laburnum.

Filled with disappointment, Anthony found his way back home. He didn't think Miranda would want to marry him now, but he was wrong. Miranda thought Anthony was the bravest person she had ever met and wanted to marry him and live in the derelict cottage. And because it was now safe to enter the wood, they could make a living hunting there. So Anthony and Miranda lived happily ever after in the wizard and witch's lovely old cottage.

The Scary Scarecrow

Mark, Victoria and Sophie are having a competition to see who can make the best scarecrow. Mark would love to win but he's only four and his eight year old twin sisters seem much smarter than him. They make their scarecrows in Farmer Ben's field, and he will give a prize for the best one.

Victoria has nearly finished. Her scarecrow has a lovely pink scarf and a floppy hat, which she covers with bows and feathers.

Sophie's wears an old top hat, with matching gloves that she found in the dressing-up box. She has drawn a big smile on its pumpkin face. The two scarecrows look fabulous! Mark looks at his effort, an old brush with a scarf tied round it, and decides to go home as he's sure he won't win. Back home he draws an angry face to show how he feels. He thinks it will make a good mask, but when he puts it on it scares the cat. This gives Mark an idea.

Mark races back to the field and ties his mask to the brush, just as Farmer Ben arrives to judge their efforts. The farmer thinks the twins' scarecrows are great but he knows they won't scare the birds away, which is, of course, why we have scarecrows! So Mark's scary scarecrow wins the prize - a big bag of juicy apples, which he happily shares with his sisters! Then he goes home to draw another face. A happy smiley one this time!

Daydreaming Darren

Darren is a daydreamer. Instead of paying attention at school, he imagines being a fighter pilot or a famous lawyer; a pop star or maybe a television personality. Anything but pay attention to his lessons. One day, a famous television sports presenter visits the school to talk to the children about careers.

The guest asks the children if any of them have thought about a career as a sports presenter.

Darren's hand shoots up. The man asks him if there is a particular sport that he is good at. Darren shakes his head, he spends too much of his time daydreaming to practise much sport. The man asks if Darren is good at English or Drama. But again, Darren shakes his head, he is far too busy daydreaming to do his English homework, or maths, science, geography, or anything really.

The presenter says that if the children want to have interesting careers, the most important step is to work hard and pay attention when they are at school.

Darren thinks maybe he should concentrate in his lessons in future because he really would like to be famous like the guest. He is suddenly aware that it is very quiet in the classroom and looks up to find the lesson is over and everyone has left. Oops, Darren has been daydreaming again!

The Lost Wellies

James lives on a farm. It's often quite muddy so there are always lots of Wellington boots to be found - and lost. James always seems to lose the left boot and today he discovers that, yet again, one left boot is missing. Dad is cross and refuses to buy another new pair, so James must borrow one of Dad's spares, (which are too enormous to walk in), or borrow one of Mum's, (which are pink), or he must search again to find the lost one. He chooses the last option!

James looks everywhere until there is only the duck pond left. As he searches through the reeds, he sees his blue boot hidden near the water's edge. Bending down to retrieve it, he finds a nest of eggs inside the boot! James doesn't know what to do, as he can't disturb the nest. Then he spots something bobbing up and down near the lily pads. It's the red boot he lost last month. Hurray! Now he can wear the old red boot with the blue boot he has at home.

The Art Lesson

Today at school, the children are having an art lesson with Mrs Harper.

This is Elliott's favourite day of the week, because he's rather good at drawing and painting, and he'd love to be an artist when he grows up. Mrs Harper is having a competition to see who can paint the best picture of an Australian creature. It can be a bird, fish, insect or animal.

Mrs Harper lays out a huge pile of photographs for the children.

Nicki likes the colourful, red and yellow parrot; Chris wants to draw a big fierce looking shark; Beth picks a kangaroo with a long tail and powerful legs; and Vicki thinks it would be fun to paint a kookaburra. But Elliott just can't make up his mind. There are so many animals to choose from.

He doesn't want the pretty pink flamingo, the cute budgerigar, or the cuddly koala. He wants something that will catch the teacher's eye. Finally he finds the perfect creature. It's a very scary looking crocodile. He decides to paint the crocodile swimming in the water with its huge mouth open wide, showing rows of sharp pointed teeth. The children take the photographs back to their desks and collect some paper, brushes and paint pots.

Mrs Harper is very pleased with the children's paintings and hangs them all around the classroom. It's difficult for her to choose the winning picture because they are all so good. But then she comes to Elliott's painting and it is the best by far.

Mrs Harper gives first prize to Elliott. He wins a big bag of sweets, which he happily shares with all his classmates during break time.

Alien Invasion

James longs to be a spaceman. He has lots of books about astronauts and his bedroom walls are covered with pictures of planets and rockets. He loves make-believe games about space.

One day, he runs into the garden wearing a homemade space suit, ready to tackle any fierce monsters. James doesn't know it yet, but today he's going to meet some real aliens!

Out in deepest, darkest space, an alien spaceship approaches our solar system.

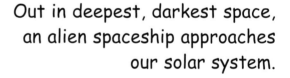

It has been travelling for many years, looking for a new planet to live on. The creatures on the ship built the largest machine that has ever been seen on their planet. Inside, there is a city with roads, gardens and room for them and all their animals and crops too. Now the captain thinks he has found a planet that looks very nice.

The captain lands the ship near a lake, in an area covered with tall, green plants. The aliens climb down the ladder to look around. Suddenly, the sky darkens and deafening thunder shakes the ground. Terrified aliens scramble up the ladder to safety. This planet is much too scary afterall!

James is racing round the garden, fighting pretend aliens, when he senses something whizz past his nose and land next to a puddle in the long grass.

James kneels down to take a closer look and sees a metal object, the size of an apple pip, with tiny insect-like creatures pouring out of it. As soon as his shadow falls over them, they stream back in. Then the little metal pip shoots past him, way up into the sky. 'What on Earth was that?' wonders James, as he goes back to his game. Well we know, don't we?

27

Charlie the Clown

Charlie's family have been clowns for as long as anyone can remember and it is expected that Charlie will be a clown too. The trouble is, Charlie would rather be a high wire or trapeze artiste, but no one will listen to him. So whenever he can find the time he practices balancing and walking across his mum's washing line.

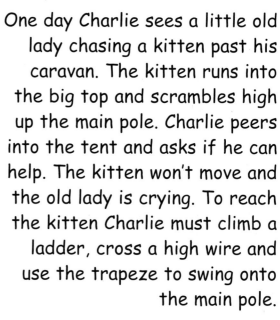

One day Charlie sees a little old lady chasing a kitten past his caravan. The kitten runs into the big top and scrambles high up the main pole. Charlie peers into the tent and asks if he can help. The kitten won't move and the old lady is crying. To reach the kitten Charlie must climb a ladder, cross a high wire and use the trapeze to swing onto the main pole.

Charlie's parents arrive just as he's about to cross the high wire. They shout at him to turn back but Charlie is concentrating too hard to hear them. He's nearly there now! Just half a metre to go, and yes, he makes it across the wire safely. Then he reaches for the trapeze and with a huge jump he launches himself high into the air. They all hold their breaths as he somersaults and lands neatly next to the little kitten.

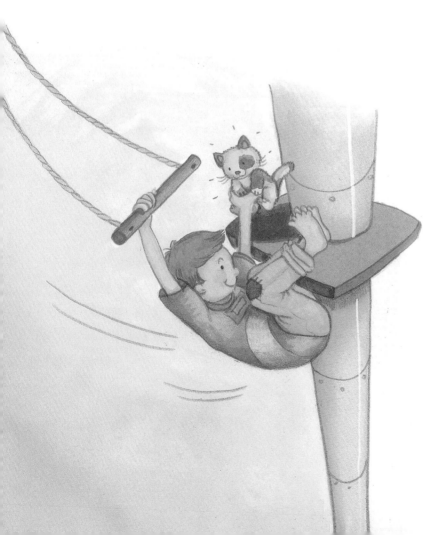

Charlie scoops the kitten into his arms and jumps off the platform onto the safety net. Everybody cheers. The little old lady says Charlie is a hero and can't thank him enough. Charlie's Mum and Dad are so impressed with Charlie's skills that they tell him he can start training for the high wire if that's what he wants. Charlie can't wait!

Tough Tommy

Tommy is a big, blue truck. He is very strong and can carry almost anything. Last week he drove two enormous elephants from one zoo to another, fifty miles away. It's all in a day's work for Tommy the truck.

Tommy likes the way that everyone looks up to him but he has a secret fear. Tommy worries that one day he might have to use his horn.

Tommy would love a great big booming horn but his just makes an embarrassing little squeak! Tommy can't bear the thought of everyone laughing at him.

To avoid using his horn, Tommy will not drive anywhere that is busy. He drives through the quiet countryside where he's unlikely to meet anyone, but this makes his journeys much longer than they need to be.

Today is Tommy's birthday and he is exactly one year old. There is going to be a big birthday party this afternoon and all the other trucks from Tommy's yard will be there. But there is one little problem. Tommy still has one last delivery to make and if he goes the long way round, he will be late for his own party. Poor Tommy, whatever should he do now?

The other trucks don't know why Tommy is so sad but to cheer him up they decide to give him their present before he leaves. He rips off the paper and can't believe his luck when he opens the box. It is a big, shiny, fabulously noisy horn! Tommy is delighted. Now he can go the shorter routes and use his horn as much as he likes. He races off with the final load and is soon back in time to enjoy his party.

Fashion Fairy

Little Fairy Lucy flutters around the snow-blanketed garden. I wonder what she is looking for? She looks very pretty in her winter clothes. She's wearing a tiny pair of green gloves made out of moss; beautiful, soft mushroom-skin boots; cobweb tights and a winter heather dress. Her clothes keep her nice and warm but her head feels rather cold. So she is searching for a winter hat.

Most of the plants and trees in the garden have gone to sleep over winter. The holly bush looks fresh and bright with its red berries, but it would make a very prickly hat! Lucy spots an acorn shell under the oak tree. It fits quite well, but Lucy suspects it probably looks a bit odd and it keeps slipping over her eyes! Finally she sees the perfect hat, poking through the snow in the rockery. It's a snowdrop. When Lucy shows it to her fairy friends, they will all want one too!

32